WORKBOOK

MAKING THE MOST OF *MOST Marriage*

DR. KEVIN LEMAN
With
GERRY PEAK

SAMPSON MINISTRY RESOURCES
4887 Alpha Road, Suite 220   •   Dallas, Texas 75244
800-371-5248   •   972-387-2806   •   FAX 972-387-0150

TABLE OF CONTENTS

HOW TO USE THIS WORKBOOK

The MAKING THE MOST OF MARRIAGE workbook accompanies the seven video
lessons by Dr. Kevin Leman and is critical to the study. This workbook will help married
couples make practical application of Dr. Leman's video lessons. Use the workbook
aggressively! Whether you are completing the study with a group of couples or on your
own, be sure to take notes on the video lessons, then work through the discussion guide,
writing down your thoughts, ideas, and comments. Fill in every blank. NOTE: Each lesson
is designed to be completed in 55 to 60 minutes, but in the event that you are unable to finish
in the allotted time, feel free to carry over to the next session or complete the lessons on your
own. May God bless you in your study of MAKING THE MOST OF MARRIAGE.

Lesson 1

DESIGNED TO BE DIFFERENT
Balancing the Challenges and Benefits of Two Distinctive Personalities

Scripture: *And the Lord God said, "It isn't good for man to be alone; I will make a companion for him, a helper suited to his needs." Genesis 2:18, TLB*

"We are designed to be different, and that's the trick."

☞ Jot down some thoughts as Dr. Leman talks about making the most of marriage.

VIEWING THE VIDEO

"Men and women see life from different perspectives, but God's Word calls us to become one."

1. Marriage is not a piece of _____. The average marriage today lasts about ____ years.

2. What's going to make your marriage different?

3. When listing the most important things in life, women listed _____ as number 14 on their list of priorities, right behind gardening.

4. Men and women view life differently. Dr. Leman's example of ordering in a restaurant.

5. Reasons why Dr. Leman enjoys being a man

6. Difference between smart husbands and dumb husbands: A smart husband will see something that needs to be done and _____.

7. Use PINK and BLUE highlighters as you engage in this study.

8. You can let differences _____ _____ _____ or you can realize that these differences are what make you a couple and that you _____ _____ _____.

DISCUSSION

1. The title of this study series is *Making the Most of Marriage*. Whether you are newly married or have been married for years, why do you want to make the most of your marriage? Jot down your thoughts and discuss with others in the group.

_____

_____

2. Dr. Leman says that the average lifespan of a marriage is 7 years. What do you believe are some reasons why marriages fail? Jot down your thoughts.

_____

_____

3. **CASE STUDY**: _Bob and Evelyn met at a company picnic and fell in love at first sight. He is the life of any party--outgoing, funny, and at ease among friends. Evelyn is a hard-working, disciplined woman who excels at everything she does. Both Bob and Evelyn saw in each other character traits that they wished they had in their own lives. Their differences attracted them to each other. But after three years of marriage, these same differences are no longer appealing. In fact, Bob thinks Evelyn is too uptight, too structured, too consumed with what people think. Evelyn resents what she sees as Bob's sloppy life-style and gets sick of his stale jokes. They lecture each other, hoping the other will change. So far – no change, just frustration and disillusionment. Friends tell them that they are just going through a "rough spot" and will grow out of it. Evelyn's father is encouraging her to issue Bob an ultimatum and threaten divorce. A woman at Bob's office has become a sympathetic listener to his expressions of marital unhappiness._ If Bob or Evelyn came to you and asked for advice on what to do about their unhappy marriage, what would you say? Write down your thoughts and discuss with others.

_____

_____

_____

_____

4. Dr. Leman admits that he made many mistakes early in his marriage, such as giving his wife Sandy her engagement ring in a field! No marriage is perfect because we all make mistakes. Thinking back on your marriage, share with the group some mistakes that you have made?

_____

_____

5. Men and women tend to view life from different perspectives. Think about differences in the way you and your spouse respond to various situations. In the columns below, compare the differences as to how you and your spouse might respond in the following situations.

Event	How He Would Respond	How She Would Respond
Friends invite you to a formal event.		
It's a beautiful Saturday with clear skies.		
Planning how to spend your vacation.		
How you want to be treated when sick.		

6. Dr. Leman says that his wife expects him to be able to "read her mind." Does your spouse have the same expectation of you? ❑ Yes ❑ No Think of reasons why this expectation may not be that unreasonable for married couples who have achieved a healthy level of intimacy. Jot down your thoughts and discuss with others.

_____

_____

7. Genesis 2:18 states: *And the Lord God said, "It isn't good for man to be alone; I will make a companion for him, a helper suited to his needs."* In the columns below, describe the ways you are a helper to your spouse and your spouse is a helper to you.

I help my spouse in these ways . . .	My spouse helps me in these ways . . .

8. Dr. Leman encourages husbands to be "turned on and tuned in" to their wives. What does being "turned on and tuned in" to one's wife suggest to you? Write down your thoughts.

_____

_____

9. Dr. Leman also says that wives want their husbands to "step up to the plate and be the men they're supposed to be?" How would you explain this statement and its meaning to a man who knows nothing about baseball but who wants to fulfill his rightful role in his marriage?

_____

_____

10. Think about ways in which you and your spouse are different. Jot down some words or phrases in the columns below that contrast your differences.

I am . . .	My spouse is . . .

11. If your spouse is participating in this session with you, turn to him or her and compare your responses in # 10 above. Put a check mark ✓ beside areas in which your responses are similar.

12. As a couple (or by yourself if your spouse is absent), read the following statement by Dr. Leman:

"God created us differently. He made us in His image. We are designed to be different, and that's the trick. We are challenged to balance the differences. It's my prayer that you will become one in marriage."

13. In the box below, write down your words to complete the prayer. Then pray with your spouse or with a small group seated nearby for the Lord's help in balancing the differences in your personalities and becoming one in marriage.

> Lord, I really want to make the most of my marriage. I thank you for my spouse and for our similarities and our differences. I pray that you will help us to become one in mind and spirit by . . .

Lesson 2

WHERE HAVE ALL THE FLOWERS GONE?

Doing Your Best for the One You Love the Most

Scripture: *"I am my beloved's and I am the one he desires."* Song of Solomon 7:10, TLB

"Where have the flowers gone in your relationship?"

☞ Jot down some notes as Dr. Leman talks about restoring romance in marriage.

VIEWING THE VIDEO

"It's so easy to become separated and get off track in marriage."

1. If things are getting _____ in your home, some things are going wrong in your marriage.

2. Men and women's needs are _____.

3. The number one need for women is _____.

4. The number two need for women is honesty and openness. She wants _____.

5. Women are _____. Their needs are wrapped up in people.

6. The number one need for men is _____ _____.

7. On the way home, discuss: "Is there a difference between sex and sexual fulfillment?"

8. The number two need for men is _____.

9. *The Five Love Languages*, by Gary Chapman

10. Married couples need to see life through their _____ _____.

11. Don't get into head knocking. Don't major on the _____.

DISCUSSION

1. Most marriages cool down from the romantic fervor of courtship. What did you and your spouse do when you were dating that you would like to resume—at least occasionally—now that you are married?

_____

_____

2. Dr. Leman says that it is easy to get separated, to get off track in marriage. Do you agree? If so, why? Jot down your thoughts and discuss with others in the group.

    _____

    _____

3. **CASE STUDY**: *Karl and Andrea believed that they were made for each other. After dating for over a year, they became engaged and were married the week before Christmas. Because of the high cost of living in their city, they both chose to work until they had saved up enough money to buy a house and start a family. They knew that the early years would be lean and that they would have to work overtime to build up the family nest egg. Along the way other needs arose: buying a car, continuing education for Karl, and caring for Andrea's aging parents. After six years of two jobs, delayed gratification, and immersion in work, Karl and Andrea realize that their marriage has become more of a corporate arrangement than a loving, intimate relationship. They feel more married to their work than to one another. When they finally have time alone, they find little to talk about and never discuss their marriage. One day Karl or Andrea admits to you, a family friend, that they don't love each other any more.* How would you respond? Write down your thoughts and discuss with others in the group.

    _____

    _____

    _____

    _____

4. Dr. Leman says that the # 1 need for women is affection. If you are a woman, describe the ways you wish your husband would express his affection for you. If you are a man, describe the ways you express affection for your wife. Compare lists with your spouse.

    _____

    _____

5. Women need honesty and openness, free-flowing communication with their husbands. Check one of the following statements that best represents the current level of communication in your marriage.

    ❑ We communicate well, and we understand the best times to talk and discuss issues.
    ❑ We talk every day, but we are not really communicating on a meaningful level.
    ❑ We need to talk more, but we can't seem to find the time.
    ❑ Talk? What's there to talk about?

6. If your marriage could use more honesty, openness, and meaningful conversation, write down some possible days and times when you and your spouse would be most available to one

another. Discuss these times with your spouse and make a commitment to set aside uninterrupted time to talk to and to listen to one another.

Days of the Week	Time of Day

7. Dr. Leman says that the number one need for men is sexual fulfillment but that sexual fulfillment is not necessarily the same thing as sex. Do you agree or disagree? Jot down your thoughts and discuss your response with your spouse. I ❏ agree ❏ disagree because

_____

_____

8. The # 2 need of men is respect. If you are a man, how does your wife show respect for you? If you are a woman, how do you show respect for your husband? Write down your responses and discuss them with your spouse.

_____

_____

9. Do you agree with the findings that Dr. Leman shared regarding a man's first and second greatest needs? Would you place these needs in a different sequence? Explain your answer in the space that follows and discuss with the group.

_____

_____

10. *The Five Love Languages* by Gary Chapman lists the five most common ways people express love for one another. Review the list below and circle two ways you wish your spouse would express love for you. Compare your responses with your spouse and ask your spouse how you can be more effective in expressing love in his/her love language.

      Physical touch   Quality time together   Acts of service

          Words of affirmation   Giving gifts

11. Dr. Leman says that men are not just interested in sex; they are interested in being wanted and in being needed. If you are a woman, how do you express to your husband that you need him? If you are a man, what does your wife do or say that proves she needs you? Write down your responses and compare them with your spouse's responses.

_____

12. How adept are you at seeing life through your spouse's eyes? Check the responses that reflect your ability to understand your spouse's point of view.

- ❑ I don't have a clue. He/She is a mystery to me.
- ❑ At times I think I have him/her figured out, but later I learn that I really don't.
- ❑ At times I can predict how he/she is going to respond. I'm beginning to see life through his/her eyes.
- ❑ After all of these years I can truly say that I can see life through my spouse's eyes. I know how he/she will respond in almost any situation.

13. Review your notes and responses in this session. Think about how you can improve the way you meet your spouse's needs, and then complete the statement below. Share your response with your spouse and close the session by praying together. Ask the Lord to change your heart so you can contribute to greater unity in your marriage.

> Rather than try to change my spouse, I want to change myself and do a better job of meeting my spouse's needs. This session has helped me realize that I can help both of us enjoy the journey of marriage by . . .

Lesson 3

STRIKING THE PERFECT MATCH
How Birth Order Affects Who You Are and the Marriage of Your Dreams

Scripture: *"And why worry about a speck in the eye of a brother when you have a board in your own."* Matthew 7:3, TLB

"When we get <u>real</u> and understand our differences, then we have an opportunity to communicate and work things out."

☞ Jot down some notes as Dr. Leman talks about the impact of birth order.

VIEWING THE VIDEO

"Our job is to love people the way they are with all their spots and blemishes."

1. First-borns are the _____ _____ of life. We practice on them.

2. Only children are like first-borns in _____.

3. Middle children are _____ right in the middle.

4. Many of today's comedians were _____ in their families.

5. God makes each person unique.

6. The baby of the family tends to be manipulative, _____, and outgoing.

7. Only-children usually relate to older friends rather than to their peers.

8. It's not two people who marry; it's at least _____.

9. If you are a first-born, watch your _____ eye.

10. Understand each other's differences according to birth order. Be patient with one another.

DISCUSSION

1. What is your position in the birth order of your family? ❑ first born, ❑ middle child, ❑ baby of the family, ❑ only child, ❑ a twin. In what ways did Dr. Leman's descriptions of your birth order characteristics match up with your own perceptions?

_____

_____

2. Dr. Leman says that God makes every person unique. In what ways do his descriptions differ from the way you see yourself. Jot down your thoughts and discuss with the group.

_____

_____

3. **CASE STUDY**: *Chase and Blair are both only-children. They were attracted to one another and began dating because they appreciated the qualities they shared. Both are hard working, conscientious, and want to please others. They have high standards, like to be organized, and dislike anything that is fake, shoddy, or of inferior quality. They felt comfortable with one another, became engaged, and then married a few months later. For the first two years of their marriage, Chase and Blair agreed on nearly every decision they faced. It was almost as if they could complete each other's sentences after only a few words were spoken. Lately they have come into conflict over seemingly trivial matters. Chase does not keep his side of the closet as clean as he used to. Blair has experimented with a different hair color that Chase dislikes. Chase wants to try eating out at different restaurants, and Blair does not. Blair wants to wallpaper the bedroom, but Chase prefers the current painted walls. Neither will budge, and both are growing increasingly angry and disillusioned in their marriage.* What is going on in this marriage and how can an understanding of birth order help this couple solve their disagreements? Write down your thoughts and discuss with the group.

_____

_____

_____

4. If you are married, what is your spouse's position in the birth order of his/her family? ❑ first born, ❑ middle child, ❑ baby of the family, ❑ only child, ❑ a twin. In what ways are Dr. Leman's descriptions of your spouse's birth order accurate in describing your spouse?

_____

_____

5. In what ways does your spouse differ from the usual characteristics of his/her birth order?

_____

_____

6. Think about the commonalities or differences in your and your spouse's birth order. Complete either statement (1) or (2) below. After completing the appropriate statement, discuss your responses with your spouse and with others in the group.

(1) My spouse and I share the same birth order position in our families. Our similarities have made our marriage . . .

_____

_____

(2) My spouse and I occupy different birth order positions in our families. Our differences have made our marriage . . .

_____

_____

7. In you have children, write each child's name in the appropriate box in the left column. Then check the corresponding characteristics in the right column that accurately describe each child. After the word "Uniqueness," describe how each child is unique or breaks the birth order mold.

Child's Name	Common Birth Order Characteristics
First Born or Only Child:	❑ Achiever ❑ Perfectionist, can be highly critical ❑ High aspirations ❑ Seeks to please ❑ Well-mannered, polite **Uniqueness:**
Middle Child(ren):	❑ Mediator ❑ Negotiator ❑ Not many photos in the family album ❑ Always lands on his/her feet ❑ Non-conformist, rebel, maverick **Uniqueness:**
Baby of the Family:	❑ Comedian, makes us laugh ❑ Social, outgoing, never meets a stranger ❑ Entertaining ❑ Manipulative ❑ Convincing, a great salesperson **Uniqueness:**

8. Dr. Leman says that fathers leave a lasting imprint on their daughters, and mothers leave a lasting imprint on their sons. As you think about your family, do you agree or disagree with this statement? ❑ Agree ❑ Disagree Explain your answer below and discuss with the group.

_____

_____

9. Every person brings to marriage an unwritten but highly developed rulebook. Think about the unwritten rulebooks you and your spouse brought to your marriage. It may have taken a while for the two of you to realize that you were living or "playing" by different rules. In the space below, write down a couple of rules that your spouse brought to your marriage that have led to changes in your life. Share your responses with your spouse and the group.

_____

_____

10. Some couples make life miserable for one another by "majoring on the minors," by nit-picking and focusing on a spouse's flaws. Dr. Leman says that perfectionism is "slow suicide" and is a great way to defeat yourself. If you and your spouse have been majoring on the minors, make a list of at least three actions you can take to get out of the "minor leagues" and bring greater harmony to your marriage.

(1) _____

(2) _____

(3) _____

11. **CASE STUDY**: *Your second child Audrey has been a delight to you and a good playmate to your first-born Stephanie. But something unexplainable happened after Mason, your third child, was born. Audrey's well-mannered personality deteriorated into a child terrorist. She started fighting with Stephanie, pinching Mason and making him cry, and talking back disrespectfully to you and your spouse. She has been getting in trouble at school, but rather than talk about her anger, Audrey just "clams up," locks herself in her room, and cries. Stephanie delights in tattling on her younger sister's exploits and playing with her younger brother Mason. You and your spouse have reasoned with Audrey and disciplined her until you are exhausted and frustrated but without any outward signs of success. Another couple with three children has suggested putting Audrey in a private school or taking her to a child psychologist.* What do you think needs to be done with Audrey? Jot down your thoughts and discuss with the group.

_____

_____

12. Matthew 5:48 states: *"But you are to be perfect, even as your Father in heaven is perfect."* Dr. Leman says that Chuck Swindoll told him that the meaning of "perfect" in this scripture relates to growing, striving, and maturing. Based on what you have learned about yourself, your spouse, your children, and the impact of birth order on family relationships, read and complete the following prayer. Share your response with your spouse, and then pray together. Ask God to help both of you grow and mature as a couple and as parents.

> Lord, I know that I am far from perfect, but I also know that I can grow and mature. Please help me to understand myself more fully and to show more grace to my spouse and children. I commit to You that I will strive to . . .
>
>
>
>
>
>
>
> Amen.

Lesson 4

LOOKING FOR LOVE IN TWO SPECIAL FACES

How Kids Grow and Thrive Through Mom and Dad's Relationship

Scripture: *"A man must love his wife as a part of himself; and the wife must see to it that she deeply respects her husband—obeying, praising, and honoring him."* Ephesians 5:33b, TLB

"A marriage that is good for you as a couple is even better for your kids."

☞ Jot down some notes as Dr. Leman talks about how you can help your kids thrive.

VIEWING THE VIDEO

"Kids find out what a marriage is supposed to be by watching their parents."

1. Most TV shows picture dads as _____.

2. One of the major fears of youth today is that their _____

   _____ _____.

3. Most marriages today last only _____ years.

4. If you want your child to have healthy self-esteem, be a couple. Be on the same page.

5. Every kid needs vitamin N -- _____

6. Many of us are trapped in the tyranny of the urgent. Get out of that rat race.

7. If anyone is going to talk to a daughter about sex, it should be her _____.

8. If you want to give your children a special gift in life, show them _____ in your

   marriage.

DISCUSSION

1. Think about growing up in your family and watching your parents interact. What ideas or perceptions about marriage did you gain from your parents? Jot down your thoughts and discuss with the persons seated near you.

   _____

   _____

2. When you think about the influence that your parents' marriage had on you and your ideas about marriage, what changes—if any—would you like to see in your marriage to provide your children an environment in which to grow and thrive?

_____

_____

3. **CASE STUDY**: *Broderick grew up living with his mother when his parents divorced. Broderick's wife Amanda grew up in foster homes, never knowing her parents. The first six months of their marriage were like an extended honeymoon for Broderick and Amanda, but lately signs have increased that the honeymoon is over. When Amanda gets angry, she yells and sometimes threatens to leave Broderick. Broderick doesn't understand Amanda's moods and threats. Rather than argue with her, he does whatever he can to calm the situation and restore the relationship. Broderick tries to control his temper and not insist on getting his way. After three years of marriage, Amanda's satisfaction with married life is high, but Broderick has become bitter and resentful. The last thing he wants is for his marriage to end in divorce, but he finds living with Amanda increasingly unbearable. He finds reasons to stay late at work or to go into the office on the weekends just to avoid being with Amanda.* What do you think is needed to restore Broderick and Amanda's marriage and rebuild their relationship? Jot down your thoughts and discuss with the group.

_____

_____

_____

_____

4. Dr. Leman says that he cannot understand how people can have healthy marriages without making Christ the center of the home. If a married couple wants to make Christ the center of their home, what are some steps they should take? Write down some ideas below and discuss with the group.

   (1) _____

   (2) _____

   (3) _____

   (4) _____

5. Most marriages last only seven years. What do you believe are the primary reasons why many marriages fail? Jot down your thoughts in the spaces below.

_____

_____

6. How will your marriage avoid becoming a divorce statistic? What actions are you and your spouse taking that will help your marriage endure? Write down your thoughts and discuss with the group.

_____

_____

7. Dr. Leman tells parents not to nag their children. He also says that every child needs vitamin N – being told "No." These two ideas may appear to be contradictory. How can parents keep from nagging their children yet still administer vitamin N whenever needed? Jot down your thoughts and discuss your ideas with the group.

_____

_____

8. Life today seems more hectic and frantic than it has ever been, with many families feeling like they are trapped in the tyranny of the urgent. Moms are often referred to as taxi drivers, and most every dad believes he does not have enough time with his children. Which of the following statements sounds most like your family? Check all that apply.

   ❑ I want our kids to have opportunities that I never had, so being busy is just part of life.
   ❑ Our kids love sports, so we have to spend lots of time on the road and at practice sessions.
   ❑ My spouse and I have to work to pay our bills. There are just not enough hours in the day.
   ❑ Being busy is just a season of our lives today. We'll be able to slow down later.
   ❑ I would love to slow down the pace of life, but I don't know where to begin.
   ❑ If my kids and spouse want to go somewhere or do something, I can't say "no."
   ❑ We found freedom from the tyranny of the urgent by . . .

   _____

   _____

9. Every married couple experiences conflict. When you and your spouse disagree or engage in a heated, verbal argument, how do you usually resolve the issue?

   _____

   _____

10. If you have children, how do your disagreements affect your children? _____

   _____

11. What do you want your children to learn about conflict and conflict resolution in marriage? Write down your thoughts and discuss with the group.

_____

_____

12. Dr. Leman says that children will thrive and develop healthy self-esteem if they have parents who are together and on the same page. Write down some ideas about how you and your spouse can increase your unity and strengthen your compatibility and togetherness. Discuss your thoughts with your spouse and with the group.

_____

_____

13. Close this session by praying with your spouse. Use the following prayer thought to begin your prayer, finishing the prayer as you desire. Feel free to confess past mistakes and ask God's forgiveness. Remember 1 John 1:9, TLB . . .

But if we confess our sins to him [Jesus], he can be depended on to forgive us and to cleanse us from every wrong.

Lord, we want to provide our children a safe place where they can grow to love You and to love others. Help us as a couple to be on the same page so we can help our children thrive and develop healthy self-esteem. Thank you for . . .

Amen.

Lesson 5

DON'T ROCK THE JUKEBOX!
Resolving Conflicts by Turning On and Tuning In

Scripture: *"Instead, be kind to each other, tender-hearted, forgiving one another, just as God has forgiven you because you belong to Christ."* Ephesians 4:32, TLB

"Marriage is an artistic dance. It's easy to get out of kilter."

☞ Jot down some notes as Dr. Leman talks about resolving conflicts in marriage.

VIEWING THE VIDEO

"Feelings draw us together. Judgments push us apart."

1. What happens if you shake a jukebox?

2. Women are like miracle plants that need the proper _____.

3. Women want men to use words in _____. Most couples do not communicate well.

4. Books by Leman: *The New Birth Order Book*, *Sex Begins in the Kitchen*, and *Sheet Music*.

5. *Why Am I Afraid to Tell You Who I Am?* by John Powell

6. Every couple needs vitamin C -- _____.

7. Men need to listen to women because women don't always speak _____ _____.

8. Our main sex organ is our _____; it's the doorway to intimacy.

9. Ways to resolve conflict

10. "The Ten Commandments of a Couple of Promise"

DISCUSSION

1. Sometimes miscommunication between husband and wife can create funny situations and even laughter. Think of a time when you and your spouse misunderstood one another and ended up laughing about it. Describe the situation in the space below and discuss it with the group.

_____

_____

2. Marriages--like the jukebox Dr. Leman refers to--are fragile and require attention and care. Think for a moment about the level of stability and "tender loving care" in your marriage today. Check the statement that best describes the current level of care being expressed in your marriage. Discuss your response with your spouse.

☐ Our jukebox has been "out of order" for a while.
☐ Our jukebox has been battered a lot but the music still plays – sometimes.
☐ Our jukebox needs some repair work, but I have hopes it can last a lifetime.
☐ Our jukebox gets neglected sometimes, but we usually take good care of it.
☐ We've learned to baby our jukebox and take good care of it. It plays great music!

3. **CASE STUDY**: *When friends think about Larry and Melanie, they often compare them to the married couple on the TV show " Married with Children." At backyard cookouts or social events, liquor always gets Larry and Melanie talking about their dismal marriage. Larry keeps the men laughing with stories about Melanie's out-of-control spending habits and kitchen disasters. Melanie always has a group of women around her, too, as she jokes about Larry's laziness and failures in the bedroom. The two of them are the life of the party, and their putdowns of each other have become legendary. Few people take their wise cracks seriously because Larry and Melanie have been married for sixteen years and are still together. In fact, some couples whose marriages are far from fulfilling don't feel as bad about themselves because Larry and Melanie's marriage seems much worse. Recently, you and your family moved into Larry and Melanie's neighborhood and have been invited to one of these backyard cookouts.* Will you accept or decline the invitation? If you go to the cookout, how do you relate to these couples? Jot down your thoughts and discuss them with the group.

_____

_____

_____

_____

4. In John Powell's book, *Why Am I Afraid to Tell You Who I Am?*, he writes about levels of communication, from talking in clichés to complete emotional honesty. On the following scale, circle the level where you and your spouse communicate.

1	2	3	4	5	6	7	8	9	10
Clichés								**Complete emotional honesty**	

5. Dr. Leman says that for couples to become good communicators they must "turn on and tune in." Describe what the phrase "turn on and tune in" suggests to you?

_____

_____

6. The illustration of the wife who asked her husband "Do you want to stop for ice cream?" exemplifies a point about how women communicate. What lessons can be learned from this simple story?

_____

_____

7. Couples improve in the art of resolving conflict by practicing good conflict resolution skills. Marriage presents couples lots of opportunities to practice. Dr. Leman describes the method printed below. (When you have an opportunity, print this process on an index card, tape it to your refrigerator, and use it to help resolve your next conflict.)

   (1) Set a time to discuss the conflict when both of you are calm and able to focus clearly.
   (2) Sit face to face without any distractions or interruptions.
   (3) One spouse talks and the other spouse listens without interrupting.
   (4) When the first spouse has finished, the other spouse repeats what he or she has heard.
   (5) The first spouse confirms or continues to clarify until the other spouse clearly understands.
   (6) Then the spouse who has been listening speaks while the one who talked first listens without interrupting.
   (7) Both persons continue this process until both clearly understand one another and can begin resolving the conflict with love and respect for each another.

   > *If you are angry, don't sin by nursing your grudge. Don't let the sun go down with you still angry—get over it quickly; for when you are angry you give a mighty foothold to the devil.* Ephesians 4:26-27, TLB

8. Healthy conflict resolution can be hard work. Sometimes couples find it easier to turn the other way and not deal with a troublesome issue. They sweep the problem under the rug. Perhaps now is a good time to take a peek under the rug. Jot down some words or phrases that identify issues you and your spouse need to resolve.

   (1) _____   (3) _____

   (2) _____   (4) _____

   Commit to your spouse that you will use the process in # 7 above to attempt to resolve at least one of these issues this week.

9. Couples who are happily married have developed the ability to forgive one another. The greatest obstacle to forgiveness is pride. Read the words of Christ in the left column below. Then summarize Jesus' message by writing this truth in your own words in the right column.

> *Your heavenly Father will forgive you if you forgive those who sin against you; but if you refuse to forgive them, he will not forgive you.* Matthew 6:14-15, TLB

10. Dr. Leman challenges couples to "go after the problem without going after each other." When anger enters the conflict, couples can spend more time attacking one another than focusing on the problem. The statements below are personal attacks that do not really address the problem. In the space under each statement, write another statement that addresses the problem without attacking the person. (TIP: Try to avoid using the word "you.") Discuss your responses with the group.

You live like a pig! Just look at this mess you've made in my house!

_____

You cook like an arsonist: you burn everything! What's wrong with you?!

_____

You are so conceited! All you ever think about is yourself! You never ask what I want to do.

_____

Your father may have been Mr. Perfect, but I'm not! I'm sick of your constant criticism!

_____

11. Close this session by praying with your spouse. Invite the Lord into your lives, into your marriage, and into your conflicts. Remember these words from Isaiah 1:18-19, TLB.

> *Come, let's talk this over! says the Lord; no matter how deep the stain of your sins, I can take it out and make you as clean as freshly fallen snow. Even if you are stained as red as crimson, I can make you white as wool! If you will only let me help you, if you will only obey, then I will make you rich!*

Lesson 6

SEX BEGINS IN THE KITCHEN!
How to Light the Fire and Keep the Flame Burning

Scripture: *"Remember that you and your wife are partners in receiving God's blessings, and if you don't treat her as you should, your prayers will not get ready answers."*
1 Peter 3:7b, TLB

"A sexually satisfied partner rarely wanders."

☞　　Jot down some notes as Dr. Leman talks about sexual intimacy.

VIEWING THE VIDEO

"Marriage is a high stakes relationship. So many people are counting on you to be a successful couple."

1. Sex really is a _____ _____ God. Human sexuality was God's idea.

2. Tell your children that sex is good, but frame it in the context of marriage.

3. When needs are not met in marriage, they are going to be _____ in some other form.

4. It's a smart man who will ask his wife for _____ _____.

5. Share a _____ with your wife, and it will draw you closer together.

6. Women: _____ sex with your husband. Call him at work.

7. A man wants to know that he is _____ by his wife.

8. We have an _____ to do everything we can to light the fire and keep the flame burning in marriage.

DISCUSSION

1. Some couples have never talked to one another about their sexual needs. Other couples are very open with one another about their needs. Why do you think some couples shy away from the subject and other couples speak freely about it?

   _____

   _____

2. Dr. Leman encourages men to "learn" to love their wives. He encouraged men to rub their wives' feet, to leave them notes of appreciation, to scratch their backs, to be conversational with them, to listen to them, and to show them kind consideration in the morning. What do these activities have to do with learning to love your wife? Jot down some thoughts and discuss with the group.

_____

_____

3. **CASE STUDY**: *Tim read Dr. Leman's book* <u>Sex Begins in the Kitchen</u> *and decided to try some of Dr. Leman's suggestions for lighting a fire in his marriage with Katie. Katie was bewildered when Tim brought her breakfast in bed and washed all of the dirty dishes. He left her notes of appreciation in the bathroom, on the refrigerator, on the dashboard of her car, and in her purse. He rubbed her feet and her shoulders after she returned from a hard day teaching school. Rather than ask her to cook supper, he ordered pizza delivered to their home and rented a video that he knew she loved. Halfway through the movie, Katie fell asleep and started snoring, so Tim carried her upstairs and tucked her into bed. Undeterred, Tim repeated similar loving actions the next day, only this time it was home delivered Chinese food and figure skating on TV. Katie fell asleep before 9 PM, snored like a horse, and Tim carried her up to bed again. So much for the "great experiment," he thought. He tossed Leman's book in the trash compactor and stayed up late to surf pornographic sites on the internet.* What, if anything, went wrong with Tim's "great experiment?" What advice do you have for Tim and Katie? Write down your thoughts and discuss with the group.

_____

_____

_____

4. Dr. Leman challenges women to initiate sex with their husbands, to call them at work, to tell them that they need them; even kidnap them and take them out of town for the weekend. A woman should do whatever she can to spark her husband's interest. Check the statement(s) below that most accurately reflect your attitude about these suggestions.

   ❑ I bet only one in a hundred married women have ever done this.
   ❑ This is a pipe dream. Get real!
   ❑ Sounds like something an over-sexed man would want.
   ❑ Great ideas! My spouse and I have done these things several times.
   ❑ I wish! I wish!

5. Routine is the enemy of intimacy in marriage. Every married couple falls into a familiar rut or routine, especially after years of married life. How can a husband and wife team up to conquer this enemy, especially with children at home and long hours at the office? Jot down some ideas and discuss with your spouse and then with the group.

_____

_____

6. Creativity is a valuable ally in the war against worn-out habits and boring routines. But what if you are not the creative type? What other options are available? List some options below and discuss with the group.

    (1) _____

    (2) _____

    (3) _____

7. Men need recreational companionship. Remember Dr. Leman's description of how his wife accompanies him to football games and reads a book during the game. In what other ways can a wife provide recreational companionship for her husband even if she is not really interested in the recreation itself?

_____

_____

> "When it comes to sex women are like crock pots, and men are like microwave ovens."
> – Dr. Gary Smalley

---

8. Dr. Leman says that all men are not the same, and that all women are not the same. He urges husbands to find out "who their wives are," what makes them unique, and to love them with all their heart and mind. Why must both heart and mind be engaged in this discovery process for a man to be successful in keeping the flame burning? Write down your thoughts and discuss with the group.

_____

_____

9. Dr. Leman challenges women to find out what makes their husbands tick. He reminds women that men (1) think 33 times more about sex during the day as women do, (2) are visual creatures, (3) are tuned in to the physical, and (4) prefer to have sex in the morning. Compare

this list with the needs of women in # 2 on p. 23 in this workbook. With such stark differences between men and women, is sexual intimacy and oneness really possible or just a myth? Complete the statement below that reflects your opinion.

Sexual intimacy and oneness is possible if ..	Sexual intimacy and oneness is unrealistic, if not impossible, because . . .

A sexually-fulfilled husband . . .

- ❑ Will do anything for you.
- ❑ Is a scriptural mandate.
- ❑ Will feel good about himself.
- ❑ Will take on his life work with a vigor and a purpose that is unmatched.
- ❑ Appreciates the important things in life.
- ❑ Will not wander.

10. Too many marriages flounder and fail after five to seven years. What have you learned in this session that will help you and your spouse celebrate your marriage and improve your sexual relationship? Complete the statement below, then discuss it with you spouse.

> This session has reminded me that I can enhance sexual intimacy with my spouse and achieve the oneness that God intended us to have by . . .

11. Close this session by joining hands with your spouse and praying, asking God to bless your marriage and help you "light the fire and keep the flame burning."

Lesson 7

ENJOYING THE JOURNEY
Becoming ONE in a Marriage That Will Last a Lifetime

Scripture: *"Honor Christ by submitting to each other."* Ephesians 5:21, TLB

"Marriage is not a place to exercise power over another person."

☞   Jot down some notes as Dr. Leman talks about enjoying the journey of marriage.

VIEWING THE VIDEO

"Leadership is coming home and taking the burden off your wife."

1. Expectation minus reality equals _____. Then comes license. Then comes separation. Then comes divorce.

2. The person you married is not the perfect person you thought he/she was.

3. When we are disillusioned in marriage, the grass may look greener somewhere else, but once you get there you still have to _____ _____.

4. Because of _____ _____, I can learn to accept this person who is imperfect.

5. Men: Understand who this woman is. She wants to feel that she is in good hands.

6. Women: Let your husband be the leader.

7. Some couples need a clear _____ _____, an understanding of who's going to do what.

8. Men: If your wife is staying home and taking care of the kids, she should never have to ask you for a _____. Make sure she has what she needs.

DISCUSSION

1. Dr. Leman talks about enjoying the journey of marriage. As you think about the journey that you and your spouse have taken thus far, what do you believe is the key or keys for enjoying the journey of marriage? Jot down your thoughts and discuss with the group.

_____

_____

2. It's only a matter of time before every married person encounters disillusionment. If you have ever experienced disillusionment in your marriage, how did you cope with it? How did you work through those feelings? Write down your thoughts in the space below.

_____

_____

3. **CASE STUDY**: *Before you and your wife have paid the final bill stemming from your daughter Beth's wedding, Beth calls you in tears. She says that she made a horrible mistake in marrying Carl. She and Carl have been friends since elementary school, and she thought that she loved Carl. But now after six weeks of marriage, Beth tells you that she has lost all respect for Carl and their marriage is over. Not long after returning from their honeymoon, Beth found pornographic magazines and videotapes belonging to Carl in a locker in their basement. Carl had promised to throw them away but never did. Last week, Beth discovered that Carl had accrued more than $20,000 in credit card debt, something he had never discussed with her during their engagement. Now both of them are strapped with having to pay off their indebtedness little by little. The final straw occurred yesterday when Carl told Beth that his company was transferring him to another state and they will have to move more than a thousand miles away from you, her parents. Beth sobs deeply into the phone, her dreams shattered by recent discoveries and events. She asks you if she can move back home and live with you until she can find a good attorney and file for divorce. How do you respond to your daughter? Jot down your response in the space below and discuss with the group.*

_____

_____

_____

_____

4. Reread the poem "The Wall" as read by Dr. Leman. Then answer the questions that follow:

"THE WALL"

Their wedding picture mocked them from the table, these two whose minds no longer talked to each other.

They lived with such a heavy barricade between them that neither battering ram of words nor artilleries of touch could break it down.

Somewhere, between the oldest child's first tooth and the youngest daughter's graduation, they lost each other.

Throughout the years, each slowly unraveled that tangled ball of string called self, and as they tugged at stubborn knots each hid his searching from the other.

Sometimes she cried at night and begged the whispering darkness to tell her who she was. He lay beside her, snoring like a hibernating bear, unaware of her winter.

Once, after they had made love, he wanted to tell her how afraid he was of dying, but fearing to show his naked soul, he spoke instead of the sexiness of her body.

She took a course in modern art, trying to find herself in colors splashed on a canvas, and complaining to other women about men who were insensitive.
He climbed into a tomb called "the office," wrapped his mind in a shroud of paper figures and buried himself in customers.

Slowly, the wall between them rose, cemented by the mortar of indifference.

One day, reaching out to touch each other, they found a barrier they could not penetrate, and recoiling from the coldness of the stone, each retreated from the stranger on the other side.
For when love dies, it is not in a moment of angry battle, nor when fiery bodies lose their heat.
Love dies panting, exhausted, expiring at the bottom of a wall it could not scale.

5. What do you think caused a wall to separate this married couple? _____

_____

6. Was the wall inevitable or could this couple have prevented it in the first place? Explain your answer.

_____

_____

7. Is there such a wall in your marriage? ❑ Yes ❑ No If yes, what can you and your spouse do to remove it? If no, how can you and your spouse keep a wall from ever coming between you? Write down your thoughts and discuss your responses to # 5, # 6, and # 7 with your spouse.

_____

_____

8. Dr. Leman talks about going to the dentist to have his teeth cleaned of plaque. He urges couples to remove the plaque that builds up in marriages. What do you think he means by "plaque in marriage?" Jot down your description of marital plaque and discuss it with your spouse and the group.

_____

_____

9. Some couples need clearer role definitions: What is the husband's role? What is the wife's role? Based on what you have learned thus far in this course and through Bible study, write brief, simple role definitions for yourself and your spouse in the columns below.

This Is My Role	This Is My Spouse's Role

<u>**Dr. Kevin Leman on leadership in marriage**</u>

"Men—Do not lead by proclamation. Real leadership is coming home and taking the burden off your wife, communicating with her, and helping her."

10. Take a moment to review all seven lessons in this series. In the right-hand column below, write down one simple truth that you gained from each lesson.

Lesson	Lesson Title	Truth I Learned
1	**Designed to Be Different** *Balancing the Challenges and Benefits of Two Distinctive Personalities*	
2	**Where Have All the Flowers Gone?** *Doing Your Best for the One You Love the Most*	
3	**Striking the Perfect Match** *How Birth Order Affects Who You Are and the Marriage of Your Dreams*	
4	**Looking for Love in Two Special Faces** *How Kids Grow and Thrive Through Mom and Dad's Relationship*	
5	**Don't Rock the Jukebox!** *Resolving Conflicts by Turning On and Tuning In*	
6	**Sex Begins in the Kitchen!** *How to Light the Fire and Keep the Flame Burning*	
7	**Enjoying the Journey** *Becoming One in a Marriage That Will Last a Lifetime*	

11. No husband or wife alone can build a marriage that will last a lifetime. Both husband and wife are called to submit to one another and give 100 % to make the most of their marriage. Even the best marriages need the grace and power of God to last a lifetime. After reviewing these seven sessions, take a moment to meditate on what you can do to strengthen your marriage and increase intimacy with your spouse, then complete the following statement. Sign your name and add today's date.

> I want to make the most of my marriage to _____ (your spouse's name). With the help of the Lord and focusing on the following actions, I commit to build a relationship with my spouse that will last a lifetime. Today I am committing myself to
>
> _____
>
> _____
>
> _____
>
> _____
>
> _____
>
> _____
>
> _____   _____
>
>   Name   Today's Date

12. Share your commitment with your spouse and pray together. Ask God to bless your home and to give you grace to forgive and to love one another just as Christ forgave and loves you.

Best wishes for making the most of your marriage!

- 30 -